Magic Hair

WRITTEN BY RAQUEL HUDSON
ILLUSTRATED BY ERICA HARDY-ABREU

MW00955373

Copyright © 2020 Raquel Hudson

All rights reserved. No part of this publication may be reproduced, distributed or transmitted in any form or by any means, including photocopying, recording, or other electronic or mechanical methods, without written permission of the copyright owner, except in the case of brief quotations embodied in critical reviews and certain other noncommercial uses permitted by copyright law.

Raquel Hudson | Books by RH

www.MagicHairBook.com

Book Layout © 2020 Erica Hardy-Abreu

Paperback <ISBN 9780578844589>

Ebook <ISBN 9780578844596>

This book is dedicated to all the little girls who are getting to know their magic and the little girl in every woman who needs a reminder of their sparkle every now and then.

The hair on your head is magical. It can do any and everything.

When washed, your hair can turn into smooth ringlets.

When dry, it can quickly disappear, making you wonder where did it all go?

It can grow long beyond your imagination, becoming straight as an arrow.

It can be big and fluffy like a yummy marshmallow.

Or go wild and free to match a stormy day.

It can be twisted into mazes of amazement.

Or molded into the most beautiful crown.

Short, long, curly, straight, fros, braids, twists, locks. All shapes, colors and sizes.

You name it, your hair
can be anything you want it to be.

So, explore the tricks and embrace your talent.
Because your hair...is pure magic!

CPSIA information can be obtained
at www.ICGtesting.com
Printed in the USA
BVHW090826230322
632145BV00001B/11